THE OFFICIAL
SHEFFIELD UNITED
QUIZ BOOK

THE OFFICIAL SHEFFIELD UNITED QUIZ BOOK

Compiled by
Chris Cowlin and Kevin Snelgrove

Foreword by Neil Warnock

APEX PUBLISHING LTD

Hardback first published in 2009 by
Apex Publishing Ltd
PO Box 7086, Clacton on Sea, Essex, CO15 5WN, England
www.apexpublishing.co.uk

British Library Cataloguing-in-Publication Data
A catalogue record for this book
is available from the British Library

ISBN HARDBACK: 1-906358-78-8   978-1-906358-78-5

Typeset in 10.5pt Chianti Bdlt Win95BT

Cover Design: Siobhan Smith

Printed in Great Britain by the MPG Books Group,
Bodmin and King's Lynn

Author's Note:
Please can you contact me: **ChrisCowlin@btconnect.com** if you find any
mistakes/errors in this book as I would like to put them right on any
future reprints of this book. I would also like to hear from Sheffield
United fans who have enjoyed the test! For more information on me and
my books please look at: **www.ChrisCowlin.com**

This book is an official product of Sheffield United Football Club

We would like to dedicate this book to:

All the players and staff who have worked for the club during their history.

FOREWORD

It is a great honour to be asked to write the foreword to 'The Official Sheffield United Quiz Book' compiled by Chris Cowlin and Kevin Snelgrove.

Sheffield United is a club very close to my heart and the team I supported as a boy so when I became manager in December 1999 it was a dream come true. Then in May 2006, taking the Blades into the Premiership as Championship runners-up was very fulfilling, the only thing that could have topped this achievement would be for Sheffield United to win the Premiership title.

This quiz book is a fans dream, full of fascinating facts and figures covering virtually everything! It is also an excellent reference book for people wanting to learn about this great football club. I hope you enjoy this book as much as I did it certainly had me scratching my head!

Enjoy!

Neil Warnock

Sheffield United Football Club, Manager 1999-2007

INTRODUCTION

I would first of all like to thank Neil Warnock for writing the foreword to this book. I am very grateful for his help on this project as he has always been one of my most favourite managers in the game.

I would also like to thank all the people who have provided a comment and/or review on this book (these can be found at the back of the book).

I would also like to thank Peter Pridmore and John Garrett at Sheffield United Football Club for their help during the books compilation.

I hope you enjoy this book. Hopefully it should bring back some wonderful memories!

It was great working with Kevin Snelgrove again, between us I hope we have given you a selection of easy, medium and hard questions.

In closing, I would like to thank all my friends and family for encouraging me to complete this book.

Best wishes
Chris Cowlin

www.apexpublishing.co.uk

CLUB HISTORY & RECORDS

1.   *In what year was Sheffield United formed?*

2.   *What is Sheffield United's nickname?*

3.   *What is the capacity of Bramall Lane?*

4.   *In what year did Sheffield United win their first FA Cup?*

5.   *How many League appearances, a club record, did Joe Shaw make between 1945 and 1966 for Sheffield United?*

6.   *Sheffield United's record 11-2 victory took place in 1926, against which team?*

7.   *Sheffield United's record home attendance is 68,287, at a 5th round FA Cup match on 15 February 1936 that resulted in a 3-1 win against which team?*

8.   *Who is Sheffield United's record League goalscorer with 201 goals?*

9.   *Which team is Sheffield United's main rival?*

10. *What is the postcode of the Bramall Lane stadium?*

TONY CURRIE

11.   In which year was Tony born – 1949, 1950 or 1951?

12.   How many League goals did Tony score in his Sheffield United career – 54, 55 or 56?

13.   From which club did Sheffield United sign Tony?

14.   True or false: Tony scored on his Sheffield United debut, a header against Tottenham Hotspur during February 1968 in a 3-2 home win?

15.   What was Tony's nickname during his time at Bramall Lane?

16.   What position did Tony take at Sheffield United in February 1988?

17.   How many League goals did Tony score for Sheffield United during 1969/70, having been ever present this season?

18.   What is Tony's middle name – Wayne, Walter or William?

19.   How many England caps did Tony win for his country, having scored three international goals in his career – 11, 14 or 17?

20.   For which club did Tony sign when he left Bramall Lane?

CLUB HONOURS

**Match up the Sheffield United honour
with the correct season**

21.	Division One Champions	1952/53
22.	Championship Runners-up	1897/98
23.	Division Two Runners-up	1899/1900
24.	Division Four Champions	2005/06
25.	FA Cup Winners (first time)	1988/89
26.	Division One Runners-up	1981/82
27.	Division Two Champions	1898/99
28.	FA Cup Runners-up	2008/09
29.	Division Three Runners-up	1970/71
30.	Championship Play-off Runners-up	1935/36

BRIAN DEANE

31. **What is Brian's middle name – Christopher, Christi Charles?**

32. **True or false: Brian scored the first ever Premier League goal in August 1992, against Manchester United in a 2-1 home win?**

33. **How many England caps did Brian win for his coun**

34. **How many playing spells did Brian have at Bram Lane?**

35. **For which Premier League team did Brian play between 2003 and 2004?**

36. **How many Premier League goals did Brian score for The Blades in the 1992/93 season in his 41 appearances – 10, 14 or 18?**

37. **Against which Lancashire team did Brian score a Sheffield United hat-trick in an FA Cup 3rd round away replay during January 1993?**

38. **From which team did Sheffield United sign Brian 1988?**

39. **For which Portuguese team did Brian play during 1998?**

40. **Against which East Anglian team did Brian score a Blades hat-trick in a 3-0 home win in the Premier League during January 1993?**

WHERE DID THEY GO? – 1

*Match up the player with the club he joined
on leaving Sheffield United*

41.	Alan Birchenall	Birmingham City
42.	Jon Harley	Blackpool
43.	Michael Tonge	Chelsea
44.	Alf Ringstead	Bristol Rovers
45.	Paul Peschisolido	Mansfield Town
46.	Roy Warhurst	Stoke City
47.	Fred Smith	Derby County
48.	Alan Warboys	Burnley
49.	Derek Pace	Manchester City
50.	Ephraim 'Jock' Dodds	Notts County

PADDY KENNY

51.   In what position does Paddy play?

52.   From which team did Sheffield United sign Paddy?

53.   For which international team did Paddy win seven full international caps between 2004 and 2006?

54.   In which year was Paddy born – 1976, 1978 or 1980?

55.   Which Blades manager signed Paddy for Sheffield United?

56.   For which team did Paddy play between 1997 and 1998?

57.   Sheffield United lost 2-1 away to which team when Paddy made his Blades debut?

58.   Following on from the previous question, in what year did Paddy sign for Sheffield United, initially on loan?

59.   What is Paddy's middle name – Joseph, Josh or Jason?

60.   In what year did Paddy win the Sheffield United Player of the Year award?

MANAGERS – 1

*Match up the manager with the time he was
in charge of Sheffield United*

61.	Neil Warnock	1955-58
62.	John Harris (second spell)	1973-75
63.	Teddy Davison	1999-2007
64.	Steve Bruce	1981-86
65.	Ken Furphy	1932-52
66.	Howard Kendall	1968-69
67.	Ian Porterfield	1998-99
68.	Joe Mercer	1995-97
69.	Arthur Rowley	1986-88
70.	Billy McEwan	1969-73

2009/2010

71. Which defender had squad number 40 this season?

72. With which team did Sheffield United share a 0-0 away draw on the opening day of the League season?

73. Which Sheffield United player scored a last-minute equaliser in a 3-3 home draw with Ipswich Town during September 2009?

74. Which Blades defender scored the club's only goal in a 1-0 away League win at Derby County during September 2009?

75. Who managed the club during this season?

76. Who was the club chairman during this season?

77. Which team did The Blades beat 3-1 away from home during August 2009?

78. Following on from the previous question, can you name the three Sheffield United goalscorers in the game?

79. Which midfielder wore the number 10 shirt this season?

80. Which midfielder signed for Sheffield United from Portsmouth during August 2009?

NATIONALITIES – 1

Match up the player with his nationality

81.	Bruno Ribeiro	Welsh
82.	Roger Nilsen	Belarusian
83.	Gary Naysmith	Greek
84.	Vass Borbokis	Norwegian
85.	Ernest Needham	Australian
86.	Petr Katchouro	Irish
87.	Ahmed Fathi	Scottish
88.	Dean Saunders	Egyptian
89.	Peter Boyle	Portuguese
90.	David Carney	English

2008/2009

91. Which forward scored a Blades hat-trick in a 3-0 home win over Queens Park Rangers during August 2008?

92. Which team beat Sheffield United 1-0 in the Championship play-off final in May 2009?

93. Which team did The Blades beat 2-1 on aggregate over two legs in the Championship play-off semi-finals during May 2009?

94. Which Welsh team did The Blades beat 3-0 away during March 2009?

95. Who finished as the club's highest scorer with 12 League goals in 21 starts and 2 substitute appearances?

96. In what position did Sheffield United finish in The Championship?

97. How many of their 46 League matches did the club win – 20, 22 or 24?

98. Who managed The Blades during this season?

99. Which midfielder did The Blades sign from Chesterfield during January 2009?

100. True or false: The Blades kept five clean sheets in their final five League games before reaching the play-off semi-finals?

WHERE DID THEY COME FROM? – 1

*Match up the player with the club he left
to join Sheffield United*

101.	Wayne Allison	Port Vale
102.	Brian Deane (first spell)	Fulham
103.	Gordon Cowans	Tranmere Rovers
104.	Vinnie Jones	Aston Villa
105.	Lee Hendrie	Bolton Wanderers
106.	Neil Shipperley	Wolverhampton Wanderers
107.	Marcus Bent	Doncaster Rovers
108.	Colin Addison	Crystal Palace
109.	Barry Hayles	Arsenal
110.	Gary Speed	Leeds United

DIVISION TWO RUNNERS-UP – 1970/1971

111. Who was the club captain during this season?

112. Who was the manager of Sheffield United during this season?

113. Which team beat Sheffield United to the title by just three points?

114. How many of their 42 League games did the club win – 21, 23 or 25?

115. Who finished as the club's highest League scorer with 15 goals in 42 appearances?

116. Which team did Sheffield United beat 5-1 away during September 1970?

117. The Blades paid Birmingham £40,000 to sign which player during this season?

118. True or false: Sheffield United were unbeaten in the League in their seven games during April 1971?

119. Who scored a Blades brace in a 2-1 away win over Oxford United during January 1971?

120. Was this The Blades' 82nd, 83rd or 84th season in their history?

POSITIONS IN THE LEAGUE – 1

Match up the season/points with Sheffield United's
finishing position in the League

121.	2008/09, 80 points	12th
122.	1976/77, 40 points	18th
123.	1993/94, 42 points	3rd
124.	1893/94, 31 points	20th
125.	1936/37, 46 points	6th
126.	1984/85, 44 points	5th
127.	2003/04, 71 points	11th
128,	1963/64, 43 points	7th
129.	1925/26, 46 points	8th
130.	1957/58, 52 points	10th

DIVISION TWO RUNNERS-UP – 1989/1990

131. Which Yorkshire team beat The Blades to the champions spot?

132. How many of their 46 League matches did the club win – 24, 25 or 26?

133. Which manager guided the club to this success?

134. Which Blades goalkeeper was the only player to participate in all 46 League games this season?

135. How many goals did Brian Deane score for The Blades during this season in his 45 League appearances – 17, 19 or 21?

136. Which team did Sheffield United beat 5-4 at home during September 1989?

137. Which forward scored 10 League goals in 26 appearances during this season?

138. True or false: The Blades were unbeaten in their seven games during September 1989?

139. What was the score when Sheffield United played Ipswich Town at home during August 1989?

140. Which Yorkshire team did The Blades beat 4-1 away from home during March 1990?

POSITIONS IN THE LEAGUE – 2

Match up the season/points with Sheffield United's finishing position in the League

141.	1969/70, 49 points	17th	
142.	2006/07, 38 points	2nd	
143.	2000/01, 68 points	22nd	
144.	1981/82, 96 points	18th	
145.	1951/52, 41 points	9th	
146.	1907/08, 35 points	1st	
147.	1949/50, 52 points	11th	
148.	1960/61, 58 points	6th	
149.	1991/92, 57 points	3rd	
150.	1975/76, 22 points	10th	

KEITH EDWARDS

151. In what position did Keith play during his playing days?

152. For which team did Keith play in between his two spells at The Blades, from 1978 to 1981?

153. In which year was Keith born – 1955, 1956 or 1957?

154. How many League appearances did Keith make for The Blades in his football career – 261, 281 or 301?

155. The Blades were playing against which team when Keith made his club debut during January 1976 in the FA Cup 3rd round?

156. Against which team did Keith score a brace in a 4-1 home League win during October 1977?

157. How many League goals did Keith score for Sheffield United during the 1976/77 season in his 30 League appearances – 14, 18 or 22?

158. For which team did Keith play during the 1990/91 season, making 18 League appearances and scoring 4 goals?

159. Which team did Keith join when he left Bramall Lane for the second time during 1986?

160. How many League goals did Keith score in his Sheffield United career – 123, 133 or 143?

SQUAD NUMBERS 2009/2010 – 1

Match up the player with his squad number

161.	Jamie Ward	34
162.	Keith Treacy	5
163.	Ryan France	26
164.	James Harper	7
165.	Chris Morgan	15
166.	Ian Bennett	10
167.	Andy Taylor	2
168.	Kyel Reid	13
169.	Kyle Walker	18
170.	Darius Henderson	16

2007/2008

171. Who started the season as Blades manager, only to be replaced by Kevin Blackwell in February 2008?

172. In what position did The Blades finish in The Championship?

173. How many of their 46 League games did The Blades win – 13, 15 or 17?

174. With which Essex team did Sheffield United share a 2-2 draw on the opening day of the League season at Bramall Lane?

175. Which London club did Sheffield United beat 3-0 away during November 2007?

176. Who was The Blades' top League scorer with 22 goals?

177. Which goalkeeper started the six League games that Paddy Kenny missed?

178. Which defender scored the only goal in Sheffield United's 1-0 home win against Barnsley during December 2007?

179. Which striker scored a hat-trick in a 3-0 home win over Leicester City during April 2008?

180. Following on from the previous question, this player had scored all three of his goals after how many minutes on the clock – 16, 19 or 22?

WHERE DID THEY GO? – 2

*Match up the player with the club he joined
on leaving Sheffield United*

181.	George Thompson	Tulsa Roughnecks
182.	Harry Johnson	Portsmouth
183.	Jimmy Dunne	Birmingham City
184.	Ade Akinbiyi	Bradford City
185.	David Holdsworth	Arsenal
186.	Peter Withe	Derby County
187.	Danny Webber	Chesterfield
188.	Len Badger	Huddersfield Town
189.	Alan Woodward	Burnley
190.	Keith Gillespie	Mansfield Town

PAUL STANCLIFFE

191. In what position did Paul play during his playing career?

192. What is Paul's middle name – Ian, Ivan or Ivor?

193. In which year was Paul born – 1958, 1959 or 1960?

194. How many League appearances did Paul make for Sheffield United in his football career – 268, 278 or 288?

195. What was Paul's nickname as a professional footballer?

196. From which club did Sheffield United sign Paul in 1983?

197. Which manager signed Paul for Sheffield United?

198. True or false: Paul won two full England caps during his football career?

199. For which team did Paul sign when he left The Blades?

200. How many League goals did Paul score for The Blades in his career – 9, 12 or 15?

MANAGERS – 2

Match up the manager with the time he
was in charge of Sheffield United

201.	Reg Freeman	1980-81
202.	Bryan Robson	1975-77
203.	Harry Haslam	1889-1932
204.	Jimmy Sirrell	1988-95
205.	Nigel Spackman	2007-08
206.	John Harris (first spell)	1999
207.	Martin Peters	1959-68
208.	Dave Bassett	1952-55
209.	Adrian Heath	1997-98
210.	John Nicholson (secretary)	1978-80

DIVISON THREE RUNNERS-UP – 1988/1989

211. Who managed The Blades during this season?

212. Sheffield United finished eight points behind which Division Three champions that season?

213. True or false: not one Sheffield United player participated in all 46 League appearances during this season?

214. Who scored a Blades hat-trick against Swansea City at home during May 1989 in a 5-1 home win?

215. How many of their 46 League matches did Sheffield United win – 19, 22 or 25?

216. Can you name the strike partnership that scored 46 League goals between them?

217. Following on from the previous question, against which team did these two players each score a hat-trick in a 6-1 home win during September 1988?

218. Which team did Sheffield United beat 4-1 away on Boxing Day 1988?

219. True or false: Sheffield United won at home and drew away against the League champions this season?

220. Who was the club chairman during this season?

WHERE DID THEY COME FROM? – 2

*Match up the player with the club he left
to join Sheffield United*

221.	Trevor Hockey	Luton Town
222.	Nigel Spackman	Leeds United
223.	Keith Edwards	Burnley
224.	Adrian Heath	Scunthorpe United
225.	Franz Carr	Chelsea
226.	Billy Sharp	Bury
227.	John Barnwell	Hull City
228.	Bob Hatton	Newcastle United
229.	Adrian Littlejohn	Birmingham City
230.	Rob Hulse	Nottingham Forest

DANE WHITEHOUSE

231.   In which year was Dane born – 1969, 1970 or 1971?

232.   How many League goals did Dane score in his Sheffield United career – 38, 40 or 42?

233.   Against which team did Dane score a Blades hat-trick in a 5-1 away win in the League Cup 2nd round, 1st leg, during September 1994?

234.   Who scored The Blades' second goal in a 2-0 home win against Sheffield Wednesday in Division One during November 1991, with Dane opening the scoring?

235.   How many League goals did Dane score for The Blades during the club's first Premier League season, 1992/93?

236.   Against which London team did Dane score a brace for Sheffield United in a 4-2 home win on the last day of the 1992/93 season?

237.   Against which team did Dane score a brace in a 4-2 away win during November 1996 in Division One?

238.   In what year did Dane make his Blades debut, in a match against Blackpool in a 2-1 away win?

239.   Following on from the previous question, which Blades manager handed Dane his club debut?

240.   How many League games did Dane play for The Blades in his career – 131, 231 or 331?

FA CUP WINS

Match up the season/round with the result

241. *1992/93, 5th round* **Sheffield United 3-1 Tottenham Hotspur**

242. *1988/89, 4th round replay* **Sheffield United 1-0 Arsenal**

243. *1962/63, 4th round* **Southend United 1-2 Sheffield United**

244. *1951/52, 5th round* **Sheffield United 1-0 Reading**

245. *1898/99, quarter-final* **Port Vale 1-2 Sheffield United**

246. *1935/36, quarter-final* **Sheffield United 3-1 Aston Villa**

247. *1974/75, 3rd round* **Colchester United 0-2 Sheffield United**

248. *1997/98, 5th round* **Sheffield United 2-0 Bristol City**

249. *2004/05, 3rd round* **Sheffield United 2-1 Manchester United**

250. *1995/96, 3rd round replay* **Nottingham Forest 0-1 Sheffield United**

LEN BADGER

251.   How many League appearances did Len make for The Blades in his career – 458, 460 or 462?

252.   In what year did Len make his Sheffield United debut?

253.   Following on from the previous question, Len made his Blades debut against which club, in a 3-1 away defeat in the League Cup 3rd round?

254.   Which Blades manager gave Len his Sheffield United debut?

255.   In which year was Len born – 1940, 1945 or 1950?

256.   How many times did Len represent England at under-23 level – 10, 13 or 16?

257.   Against which London team did Len score for Sheffield United in a 2-0 home win during September 1965?

258.   In what position did Len play during his playing days?

259.   How many League goals did Len score for Sheffield United in his career – 5, 6 or 7?

260.   Which club did Len join when he left Bramall Lane?

SQUAD NUMBERS 2009/2010 – 2

Match up the player with his squad number

261.	Stephen Quinn	6
262.	Ched Evans	25
263.	Gary Naysmith	12
264.	Mark Bunn	28
265.	Lee Williamson	3
266.	Matthew Kilgallon	19
267.	Jordan Stewart	4
268.	David Cottrill	23
269.	Nick Montgomery	9
270.	Glen Little	11

2006/2007

271. With which team did The Blades share a 1-1 home draw on the opening day of the season?

272. Following on from the previous question, who scored Sheffield United's first Premier League goal of the season?

273. The Blades had to wait until their seventh League game of the season to record their first League victory, beating which team 2-1 at home during September 2006?

274. Which forward scored The Blades' only goal in a 1-0 away win against Newcastle United during November 2006?

275. Which forward did Sheffield United sign from Sunderland during January 2007?

276. Rob Hulse finished as the club's highest League scorer this season, with how many goals?

277. Who managed The Blades during this season?

278. In which position did Sheffield United finish in the League – 16th, 18th or 20th?

279. Which London club did Sheffield United beat 3-0 at home during April 2007?

280. Which forward scored The Blades' only goal in a 1-0 home win against Arsenal during December 2006?

CAPS FOR MY COUNTRY

*Match up the player with the number of caps
he won for his country*

281.	Barry Hayles	86 caps for Northern Ireland (2 goals)
282.	Trevor Hockey	53 caps for Canada (11 goals)
283.	Alf Ringstead	100 caps for Zimbabwe (38 goals)
284.	Peter Ndlovu	53 caps for Norway (11 goals)
285.	Peter Withe	85 caps for Wales (7 goals)
286.	Gary Speed	29 caps for Cameroon (4 goals)
287.	Paul Peschisolido	9 caps for Wales (1 goal)
288.	Keith Gillespie	10 caps for Jamaica (0 goals)
289.	Patrick Suffo	11 caps for England (1 goal)
290.	Jostein Flo	20 caps for Republic of Ireland (7 goals)

2005/2006

291. Which striker did Sheffield United sign from Burnley during January 2006?

292. In what position did Sheffield United finish in The Championship?

293. Who won The Championship, finishing 16 points ahead of Sheffield United?

294. Which Blades player scored a brace in a 4-0 home win over Luton Town during November 2005?

295. Which two Blades players scored in a 2-1 away win over Sheffield Wednesday during February 2006?

296. Who scored The Blades' winning goal in the last minute in a 3-2 home win against Hull City during April 2006?

297. Which team did Sheffield United beat 4-1 at home on the opening day of the League season?

298. Can you name the two players that were ever present during this season?

299. Who finished as the club's highest League scorer with 11 goals?

300. How many of their 46 League games did The Blades win – 22, 24 or 26?

NATIONALITIES – 2

Match up the player with his nationality

301.	Li Tie	Ivorian
302.	Bill Foulke	Barbadian
303.	Colin Hill	Canadian
304.	Paul Peschisolido	Welsh
305.	Shaun Murphy	English
306.	Alex Forbes	Northern Irish
307.	Paul Ifill	Irish
308.	Olivier Tébily	Chinese
309.	Nathan Blake	Australian
310.	Paddy Kenny	Scottish

LEGENDS

Rearrange the letters to reveal the name of a club legend

311. **YGNL SOHDEG**

312. **ILCNO SIRMOR**

313. **ILBL LURLESS**

314. **YMJMI NAGHA**

315. **BBO ACIN**

316. **NISMO CRYTEA**

317. **NAAL NOHSKINDOG**

318. **LBII ANDERED**

319. **LIG EECRE**

320. **BATLER XOC**

PLAYING YEARS AT THE CLUB – 1

Match up the player with the period he played for Sheffield United

321.	Harry Johnson	2000-04
322.	Geoff Salmons (first spell)	1901-04
323.	Albert Nightingale	1992-99
324.	Tommy Hoyland	1931-37
325.	Michael Brown	1945-66
326.	Alan Kelly	1949-61
327.	Joe Shaw	1988-2003
328.	Bobby Barclay (first spell)	1916-31
329.	Simon Tracey	1941-48
330.	Alf Common	1966-74

ALAN KELLY

331. From which club did The Blades sign Alan in 1992?

332. How many international caps did Alan win for the Republic of Ireland – 26, 30 or 34?

333. In which year was Alan born – 1966, 1967 or 1968?

334. Which team did Alan sign for when he left Bramall Lane in 1999?

335. In what position did Alan play during his playing days?

336. Which manager signed Alan for Sheffield United?

337. Against which team did Alan make his Sheffield United debut at Bramall Lane during September 1992 in a 2-0 away defeat?

338. How many League appearances did Alan make for Sheffield United in his career – 213, 216 or 219?

339. Can you name Alan's footballing father, who played and managed Preston North End in his career?

340. True or false: Alan scored a League goal for Sheffield United during his time at Bramall Lane?

POSITIONS THEY PLAYED – 1

Match up the player with his position

341.	Graham Shaw	Winger
342.	Tony Agana	Right back
343.	Mick Speight	Goalkeeper
344.	Tony Kenworthy	Striker
345.	Paddy Kenny	Left half
346.	Jimmy Hagan	Outside left
347.	Gerry Summers	Defender
348.	Walter Rickett	Midfielder
349.	Ronnie Simpson	Left back
350.	Bill Cook	Inside forward

2004/2005

351. Who managed Sheffield United during this season?

352. In which position did Sheffield United finish in the League – 6th, 7th or 8th?

353. Who finished as Sheffield United's top scorer with 15 League goals?

354. Which Yorkshire club did The Blades beat 4-0 away during April 2005?

355. Which two players both scored braces in a 4-0 home League win over Crewe Alexandra during March 2005?

356. Which defender did Sheffield United sign from Brighton during December 2004?

357. Can you name the two Blades that were ever present during this season?

358. Which Blades midfielder scored 7 League goals in his 16 starts and 5 substitute appearances?

359. How many of their 46 League games did Sheffield United win – 20, 24 or 28?

360. Who scored Sheffield United's only goal in a 1-0 away win over Derby County during November 2004?

TOP LEAGUE APPEARANCES

Match up the player with the number of League appearances he made for Sheffield United

361.	Len Badger	536 (2)
362.	Cec Coldwell	448
363.	Ernest Needham	576
364.	Graham Shaw	409 (1)
365.	Joe Shaw	437
366.	Billy Gillespie	393
367.	George Green	439
368.	Alan Hodgkinson	464
369.	Fred Tunstall	632
370.	Alan Woodward	457 (1)

DIVISION ONE PLAY-OFF RUNNERS-UP – 1997

371. Who beat Sheffield United in the play-off final?

372. Following on from the previous question, what was the score in the game?

373. Which team did Sheffield United beat in the play-off semi-finals?

374. Who managed Sheffield United during the 1996/97 season?

375. Which London club did The Blades beat 3-0 at home during October 1996?

376. Who was the club chairman during the 1996/97 season?

377. From which club did Sheffield United sign Jan-Aage Fjortoft during this season?

378. Which Essex team did The Blades beat 3-0 at home during January 1997?

379. In which position in Division One did Sheffield United finish – 3rd, 4th or 5th?

380. Who did The Blades sign from Dinamo Minsk during this season?

PLAYING YEARS AT THE CLUB – 2

*Match up the player with the period he
played for Sheffield United*

381.	Bill Russell	**1913-21**
382.	Phil Jagielka	**1972-76**
383.	Ted Burgin	**1969-78**
384.	Mick Jones	**1949-57**
385.	George Utley	**2007-09**
386.	James Beattie	**1988-93**
387.	Keith Eddy	**1926-33**
388.	Ian Bryson	**1999-2007**
389.	Jimmy Dunne	**1962-67**
390.	John Flynn	**1957-63**

2003/2004

391. In which position in the League did Sheffield United finish – 7th, 8th or 9th?

392. Sheffield United fought back and drew 3-3 at Bramall Lane against which team, having been 3-1 down after 37 minutes, during January 2004?

393. Which club did Sheffield United beat 1-0 away on Boxing Day 2003, with Jack Lester scoring the only goal from the penalty spot?

394. Which two strikers both scored a brace in a 5-0 home win in the League against Rotherham United during September 2003?

395. Who scored a brace for The Blades in a 3-3 away draw on the last day of the League season against Preston North End?

396. Who was the club's only ever present player this season?

397. Who finished as the club's highest scorer with 12 League goals?

398. Which striker signed for Sheffield United during August 2003 from Bradford City?

399. Who managed Sheffield United during this season?

400. How many of their 46 League games did Sheffield United win – 18, 20 or 22?

POSITIONS THEY PLAYED – 2

Match up the player with his position

401.	Tony Currie	Fullback
402.	Jack Smith	Striker
403.	Jimmy Simmons	Right back
404.	James Beattie	Wing half
405.	Gil Preece	Goalkeeper
406.	Cec Coldwell	Midfielder
407.	Len Allchurch	Centre half
408.	Albert Cox	Forward
409.	Harold Pantling	Outside right
410.	Tommy Morren	Outside left

CHAMPIONSHIP PLAY-OFF RUNNERS-UP – 2003

411. Which club beat The Blades 3-0 in the final?

412. Where was the final played?

413. Which team did The Blades beat in the semi-finals, winning 5-4 on aggregate over the two legs?

414. Which two Blades both scored a brace in a 4-2 home League win over Burnley during March 2003?

415. Which team did Sheffield United beat 5-0 away during November 2002?

416. Can you name the manager in charge of The Blades during this season?

417. In what position in the Championship did The Blades finish?

418. How many of their 46 League matches did the club win – 20, 23 or 26?

419. How many League goals did Michael Brown score for Sheffield United in his 39 starts and 1 substitute appearance, finishing as the club's top scorer – 12, 14 or 16?

420. Which team did Sheffield United beat 1-0 away to record their first League win of the season during August 2002?

TOP LEAGUE GOALSCORERS

Match up the player with the number of League goals he scored for Sheffield United

421.	Jimmy Dunne	129
422.	Billy Gillespie	113
423.	Jimmy Hagan	158
424.	Alan Woodward	143
425.	Ephraim 'Jock' Dodds	127
426.	Keith Edwards	201
427.	Harry Johnson	140
428.	Joe Kitchen	117
429.	Derek Pace	105
430.	Fred Tunstall	143

ALAN WOODWARD

431. In what position did Alan play during his playing days?

432. In which year was Alan born – 1944, 1945 or 1946?

433. What was Alan's nickname while at Bramall Lane?

434. What number shirt did Alan usually wear for The Blades?

435. Against which team did Alan make his League debut for Sheffield United during October 1964 in a 3-1 away defeat?

436. Against which team did Alan score four goals in a 7-0 home win for The Blades during November 1971?

437. Alan's best League goal tally for a season was during 1969/70, with how many goals for The Blades – 14, 16 or 18?

438. Against which team did Alan score a hat-trick for The Blades in a 4-2 home win during December 1973?

439. Which American team did Alan join when he left Bramall Lane?

440. How many League goals did Alan score for The Blades in his 536 starts and 2 substitute appearances for the club – 138, 158 or 178?

HOW MUCH DID THEY PAY? – 1

Match up the player with the transfer fee paid by Sheffield United

441.	Paul Beesley from Leyton Orient, 1990	£100,000
442.	Paul Garner from Huddersfield Town, 1975	£360,000
443.	Tony Currie from Watford, 1968	£1,600
444.	Jim Brown from Chesterfield, 1974	£5,000
445.	John Flynn from Workington, 1969	£59,555
446.	Arthur Brown from Gainsborough Trinity, 1902	£80,000
447.	Keith Edwards from Hull City, 1981	£12,500
448.	Brian Gayle from Ipswich Town, 1991	£2,295
449.	Jimmy Hagan from Derby County, 1938	£26,500
450.	Simon Tracey from Wimbledon, 1988	£750,000

GARY SPEED

451.   In what year did Gary sign for The Blades?

452.   How many international caps did Gary win for Wales – 82, 85 or 88?

453.   What is Gary's middle name – Adrian, Aaron or Andrew?

454.   At which club did Gary start his football career in 1988?

455.   Which team did Gary support as a young boy?

456.   Against which team did Gary make his Blades debut, in a 0-0 away draw on New Year's Day 2008?

457.   Against which London club did Gary score The Blades' second goal in a 5-2 win away during November 2008?

458.   Against which team did Gary score Sheffield United's first goal in the first minute in a 2-1 win during September 2008?

459.   From which club did Sheffield United sign Gary?

460.   Against which team did Gary score a brace, including a penalty, in a 2-1 home win during April 2008?

NEIL WARNOCK

461. Neil was born on 1 December in which year – 1944, 1946 or 1948?

462. Where was Neil born – Doncaster, Bradford or Sheffield?

463. At which club did Neil start his professional football career in 1967?

464. In his 11-year playing career how many League appearances did Neil make – 316, 326 or 336?

465. True or false: Neil once owned a greengrocers shop in Barnsley called 'The Orange Bowl'?

466. For how many years was Neil manager of Sheffield United?

467. From 1990 to 1996 Warnock led three different teams to Wembley on five occasions, but how many finals did he win?

468. True or false: Neil is a fully qualified referee?

469. Which team did Neil manage in the Conference, taking them into the Football League in 1987?

470. Which team did Neil go on to manage after leaving Sheffield United in 2007?

CAPTAINS

Match up the season with the club's captain during that campaign

471.	1945/46	Len Badger
472.	1950/51	Stewart Houston
473.	1957/58	Bryan Gayle
474.	1964/65	Paul Stancliffe
475.	1966/67	Jack Pickering
476.	1972/73	Cec Coldwell
477.	1977/78	Harry Latham
478.	1981/82	Joe Shaw
479.	1984/85	Alan Woodward
480.	1992/93	Eddie Colquhoun

ALF RINGSTEAD

481. Alf was born in Dublin on 14 October in which year –
     1925, 1927 or 1929?

482. Alf joined Sheffield United in November 1950 from
     which Cheshire non-League club?

483. Following on from the above question, what was Alf's
     transfer fee - £1,500, £2,000 or £2,500?

484. How many League and FA Cup goals did Alf score for
     Sheffield United in total – 85, 95 or 105?

485. Alf played at international level for the Republic of
     Ireland, making how many appearances – 20, 25 or
     30?

486. In what position did Alf play at Sheffield United?

487. Alf spent eight years at Bramall Lane before joining
     which club in July 1959 for £2,850?

488. How many League appearances did Alf make for The
     Blades – 247, 257 or 267?

489. Which Sheffield United manager signed Alf in
     November 1950?

490. Against which club did Alf make his Blades debut on 2
     December 1950 in a 2-0 home win?

KEVIN BLACKWELL

491. In what position did Kevin play during his playing days?

492. In what year was Kevin appointed as Blades manager?

493. Following on from the previous question, which manager did Kevin take over from at Bramall Lane?

494. Which Yorkshire team did Kevin manage between 2004 and 2006?

495. In which year was Kevin born – 1956, 1957 or 1958?

496. What is Kevin's middle name – Patrick, Paul or Peter?

497. What was the score during Kevin's first match in charge of Sheffield United, an FA Cup 5th round tie at home to Middlesbrough?

498. True or false: Kevin took The Blades to the Championship play-off final in his first full season in charge of the club?

499. For which team did Kevin play over 200 League games between 1980 and 1986?

500. True or false: Kevin was a squad player at Bramall Lane between 2000 and 2002 but didn't actually play any games for the club?

JIMMY HAGAN

501. Jimmy was born in Washington, County Durham, on 21 January in which year – 1918, 1920 or 1922?

502. Jimmy was manager of which club from 1958 to 1962?

503. How many wartime appearances for England did Jimmy make – 8, 12 or 16?

504. Jimmy made his Sheffield United debut on 5 November 1938 in a 2-1 win against which club?

505. Jimmy scored his first goal for The Blades on 26 November 1938 in a 3-1 home win against which team?

506. How many League appearances did Jimmy make for Sheffield United – 351, 361 or 371?

507. In February 1951, which club made a British record offer of £32,500 for Jimmy, although he chose to remain at Bramall Lane?

508. In what position did Jimmy play?

509. Jimmy only had one full England cap, in an 0-0 draw away in 1948 against which opponents?

510. Jimmy was manager of which Midlands club from 1963 to 1967?

DAVE BASSETT

511.   In which year was Dave born in Stanmore, London –
        1940, 1942 or 1944?

512.   True or false: Dave played for Wimbledon during the
        1974/75 season?

513.   Which club did Dave manage before taking charge at
        Bramall Lane in 1988?

514.   Who was The Blades' manager before Dave took over
        as boss in 1988?

515.   Which team did Dave manage between 1997 and
        1999?

516.   Dave guided Sheffield United to what Division Three
        League position during his first full season in charge at
        the club, 1988/89?

517.   Which Sheffield United chairman appointed Dave as
        manager of The Blades?

518.   During October 2007 Dave was appointed assistant
        manager to whom at Leeds United?

519.   True or false: Dave guided Sheffield United to two
        promotions in his first two full seasons at the club?

520.   In what year did Dave leave Bramall Lane as
        manager?

JOE SHAW

521. Joe was born on 23 June 1928 in Murton, which is
      located in which county?

522. How many appearances in all competitions did Joe
      make for Sheffield United – 704, 714 or 724?

523. Joe made his Sheffield United League debut on 30
      August 1948 in a 2-1 defeat against which team?

524. Joe was manager of which club from 1973 to 1976?

525. How many League goals did Joe score for Sheffield
      United – 4, 8 or 12?

526. Against which team did Joe make his 600th League
      appearance for Sheffield United on 6 February 1965?

527. For which club was Joe playing when he signed for
      Sheffield United in 1945?

528. Which club did Joe manage in 1967/68?

529. In what position did Joe play?

530. How many League appearances, a club record, did Joe
      make for The Blades – 582, 612 or 632?

CHAIRMAN

Match up the season with the chairman in charge during that campaign

531.	1943/44	Reg Brealey
532.	1954/55	John Hassall
533.	1955/56	Kevin McCabe
534.	1958/59	E. Senior Atkin
535.	1969/70	Mike McDonald
536.	1975/76	Albert J. Platt
537.	1981/82	Frank Copestake
538.	1991/92	E. Blacow Yates
539.	1996/97	Dick Wragg
540.	1998/99	Paul Woolhouse

MATCH THE YEAR - 1

Match up the year with the event

541.	Alan Hodgkinson played his last League game for The Blades	2003
542.	Sheffield United were FA Cup runners-up to Arsenal	2008
543.	Umbro first sponsored the Sheffield United kit	1945
544.	Michael Tonge was born	1878
545.	Kevin Blackwell became manager of Sheffield United	1971
546.	Bramall Lane hosted the world's first ever floodlit football match	1977
547.	Cec Coldwell took charge for his second spell as acting manager	1936
548.	Sheffield United reached the semi-final of the League Cup	1973
549.	Ian Bryson was born	1983
550.	Len Badger was born	1962

COLIN MORRIS

551.   In what position did Colin play for Sheffield United?

552.   In which year was Colin born in Blyth, Northumberland
        – 1953, 1954 or 1955?

553.   At which club did Colin start his professional football
        career in 1974?

554.   From which team did Colin sign to join Sheffield
        United in 1982?

555.   How many League goals did Colin score during his first
        season at Bramall Lane – 0, 2 or 4?

556.   Which manager signed Colin for The Blades?

557.   How many League appearances did Colin make for
        Sheffield United during his career – 230, 240 or 250?

558.   Can you name Colin's son, who played for The Blades
        in the 1990s?

559.   How many League goals did Colin score for Sheffield
        United during his career – 84, 88 or 92?

560.   Which team did Colin join when he left Bramall Lane?

HOW MUCH DID THEY PAY? – 2

Match up the player with the transfer fee
paid by Sheffield United

561.	Billy Gillespie from Leeds City, 1912	£33,000
562.	James Beattie from Everton, 2007	£92,500
563.	Paul Ifill from Millwall, 2005	£200,000
564.	Steve Kabba from Crystal Palace, 2002	£3,000,000
565.	Ched Evans from Manchester City, 2009	£250,000
566.	Michael Brown from Manchester City, 2000	£500
567.	Carl Asaba from Gillingham, 2001	£4,000,000
568.	Andy Woodward from Bury, 2000	£800,000
569.	Simon Francis from Bradford City, 2004	£330,000
560.	Jamie Ward from Chesterfield, 2009	£400,000

SIMON TRACEY

571. *In which year was Simon born – 1966, 1967 or 1968?*

572. *What is Simon's middle name – Paul, Peter or Patrick?*

573. *In what position did Simon play during his playing days?*

574. *In what year did Simon sign for The Blades?*

575. *From which club did Sheffield United sign Simon?*

576. *True or false: Simon won two England caps while a Sheffield United player?*

577. *Which Blades manager signed Simon for the club?*

578. *How many of The Blades' 42 Premier League games during 1992/93 did Simon start – 5, 10 or 15?*

579. *Simon was sent off after 9 minutes in a 3-0 home defeat for The Blades during March 2002, against which team?*

580. *In which year did Simon retire from playing football – 2003, 2004 or 2005?*

MATCH THE YEAR – 2

Match up the year with the event

581.	Chris Morgan joined Sheffield United from Barnsley	1980
582.	George Utley led The Blades out for the FA Cup final	2007
583.	Sheffield United received £4 million for Phil Jagielka from Everton	1892
584.	Matthew Kilgallon was born	1929
585.	Sheffield United beat Burnley 10-0	2008
586.	Port Vale lost 10-0 to Sheffield United at Vale Park	2000
587.	Darius Henderson signed from Watford for £2 million	1947
588.	Laurent D'Jaffo signed from Stockport County for £175,000	1915
589.	Ryan France was born	2003
590.	Colin Collindridge was the Division One season's top goalscorer	1984

TONY AGANA

591. In what position did Tony play during his playing days?

592. From which club did Sheffield United sign Tony in 1988?

593. Against which club did Tony make his Blades debut during February 1988 in a 1-0 home win?

594. True or false: Tony scored the only goal for The Blades on his club debut?

595. How many League appearances did Tony make in his Sheffield United career – 118, 128 or 138?

596. Which Blades manager signed Tony for Sheffield United?

597. How many League goals did Tony score during the 1988/89 season in his 44 starts – 16, 20 or 24?

598. Against which team did Tony score a brace in a 3-0 away win during August 1989?

599. How many League goals did Tony score in his Sheffield United career – 41, 42 or 43?

600. For which club did Tony sign when he left Bramall Lane in 1991?

BLADES WINS AGAINST THE OWLS

Match up the competition/date with the result

601.	*Division One, 3 March 1934*	*Blades 4-2 Owls*
602.	*Division One, 4 October 1919*	*Blades 4-1 Owls*
603.	*Championship, 18 February 2006*	*Owls 1-3 Blades*
604.	*Division Two, 3 October 1970*	*Blades 2-0 Owls*
605.	*Division One, 4 February 1967*	*Blades 5-1 Owls*
606.	*FA Cup, 22 February 1928*	*Blades 3-0 Owls*
607.	*Division Two, 21 January 1950*	*Blades 3-2 Owls*
608.	*Division One, 8 April 1905*	*Blades 1-0 Owls*
609.	*Division Two, 5 January 1952*	*Owls 0-2 Blades*
610.	*Division One, 5 September 1964*	*Owls 1-2 Blades*

PHIL JAGIELKA

611. In which year was Phil born in Greater Manchester – 1981, 1982 or 1983?

612. For which team did Phil sign when he left Bramall Lane in 2007?

613. True or false: Phil has been capped at full international level for England?

614. What is Phil's middle name – Norman, Nikodem or Nicholas?

615. Against which team did Phil make his Blades debut in May 2000 in a 0-0 home draw?

616. How many League goals did Phil score in his Blades career – 8, 18 or 28?

617. Against which team did Phil score a brace in a 3-0 home win for The Blades during March 2002?

618. Against which Yorkshire team did Phil score one of Sheffield United's last-minute goals in a 2-1 win at home during November 2002?

619. True or false: Phil was named in the 2006 PFA Championship Team of the Year?

620. Which Sheffield United manager handed Phil his club debut?

MATCH THE YEAR – 3

Match up the year with the event

621.	Jimmy Johnston joined The Blades from San Jose Earthquakes	1918
622.	Bruce Dyer joined The Blades from Stoke City	1926
623.	Derek Hawksworth made his 255th and last League appearance for Sheffield United	2006
624.	Cliff Mason left The Blades to join Yorkshire rivals Leeds United	1999
625.	Harold Pantling became Sheffield United's first player to be sent off twice in a season	2001
626.	Lee Morris was sold to Derby County for £3 million	1962
627.	The Blades launched a fellowship for former players	1975
628.	Sheffield United were relegated from the Premiership for the first time	2008
629.	Robert Page joined The Blades from Watford for £350,000	1958
630.	Roy Warhurst was born	1994

MICHAEL BROWN

631. In which year was Michael born in Hartlepool – 1976, 1977 or 1978?

632. For which London Premier League side did Michael sign when he left Bramall Lane in 2004?

633. In what position does Michael play?

634. What is Michael's middle name – Robert, Ryan or Ross?

635. At which team did Michael start his professional football career, before joining Sheffield United in 2000?

636. True or false: Michael was loaned to Sheffield United before joining them on a permanent basis?

637. Against which team did Michael score his first Blades goal in a 1-0 home League win during January 2000?

638. Can you name the manager that signed Michael for The Blades?

639. How many League goals did Michael score for Sheffield United during the 2002/03 season – 12, 14 or 16?

640. Against which team did Michael score a penalty for The Blades in a 2-1 home League win during August 2003?

POT LUCK – 1

641. Which player joined Sheffield United on a three-month loan from Stoke City in September 2009?

642. Which Norwegian player joined The Blades in January 1997 for £700,000?

643. How many League goals did Derek Hawksworth score for The Blades – 68, 78 or 88?

644. In which year did Sheffield United introduce white shorts to their kit?

645. Which stand at Bramall Lane was officially opened in 1997?

646. Which club did Claude Davis join from Sheffield United in July 2007 for £3 million?

647. From which club did Simon Francis sign to join Sheffield United for £200,000 in 2004?

648. In what position did Ron Simpson play for Sheffield United (1958-65)?

649. Which Welsh club did Gil Reece leave to join Sheffield United in 1965?

650. In which year did Sheffield United open the new South Stand?

TREVOR HOCKEY

651. **In which year was Trevor born -1941, 1942 or 1943?**

652. **In what position did Trevor play during his playing days?**

653. **For which country did Trevor win nine full international caps, scoring one goal?**

654. **From which Midlands club did Trevor sign when he joined Sheffield United in 1971?**

655. **Which manager signed Trevor for Sheffield United?**

656. **How many League appearances did Trevor make for Sheffield United in his career – 58, 68 or 78?**

657. **For which club did Trevor sign when he left Bramall Lane in 1973?**

658. **Against which team did Trevor make his Blades debut, in a 2-1 away win during January 1971?**

659. **Can you name the club where Trevor started his professional football career in 1960?**

660. **How many League goals did Trevor score for Sheffield United in his career – 2, 4 or 6?**

BLADES GOALKEEPERS

661. How many League appearances did Alan Kelly make for Sheffield United - 206, 216 or 226?

662. Which goalkeeper also made four appearances for Derbyshire playing cricket?

663. Which Dutch goalkeeper did Sheffield United take on trial during July 2009?

664. Which goalkeeper made 203 consecutive appearances for Sheffield United between 1935 and 1949?

665. Which goalkeeper made his first team debut in September 1904, eventually taking the number one position from Bill Foulke?

666. How many appearances did Alan Hodgkinson make for England – 5, 10 or 15?

667. From which club did Sheffield United sign Harold Gough in 1913?

668. How many League and Cup appearances did Ted Burgin make for Sheffield United between 1949 and 1957 – 314, 334 or 354?

669.   Which USA team did Jim Brown join in 1979?

670. Which goalkeeper signed for Sheffield United in August 2006 on a free transfer from Leeds United?

MICK JONES

671. How many full international caps did Mick win for England in his career?

672. What is Mick's middle name – Daniel, Duncan or David?

673. For which Yorkshire team did Mick sign when he left Sheffield United in 1967?

674. In what position did Mick play during his playing days?

675. True or false: Mick managed Sheffield United in the 1980s?

676. In which year was Mick born – 1943, 1944 or 1945?

677. How many League goals did Mick score for The Blades in the 1965/66 season -19, 20 or 21?

678. Against which club did Mick make his Blades debut during April 1963 in a 1-1 draw?

679. Against which club did Mick net his first goal for Sheffield United, scoring a brace in only his second game for the club during April 1963 in a 3-1 home win?

680. How many League goals did Mick score in his 149 starts for the club – 43, 53 or 63?

WHO AM I?

681. I joined Sheffield United in April 1894 as a goalkeeper and made 299 League appearances.

682. I signed for Sheffield United in September 2009 from Charlton Athletic.

683. I played 21 League games for The Blades in season 1995/96. I also won the European Cup with Aston Villa.

684. I started my career at Bramall Lane in 2006 but never played a first team game before moving on to Bury in 2008.

685. I am a midfielder and played for Hull City before joining Sheffield United on 24 July 2009.

686. I made 50 League appearances and scored 8 goals for Sheffield United before moving on to Derby County in 2008.

687. I missed the 1915 FA Cup final due to a broken leg, but returned to captain the 1925 FA Cup final win against Cardiff City.

688. I joined Sheffield United from Helsingborgs for £1,850,000 in January 2007.

689. I am a right winger who played for The Blades from 1981-87 my son Lee also played for Sheffield United.

690. I left Sheffield United in August 2008 to join Reading for £500,000.

CHRIS MORGAN

691.   What is Chris's middle name – Peter, Paul or Patrick?

692.   In what position does Chris play?

693.   From which club did Chris sign when he joined The Blades?

694.   In what year did Chris sign for The Blades?

695.   Which squad number did Chris wear while playing for Sheffield United during 2009/10?

696.   What was the score when Chris made his Sheffield United debut against Gillingham?

697.   Against which East Anglian team did Chris score Sheffield United's 90th-minute equaliser in a 3-3 home draw during September 2009?

698.   Against which team did Chris score The Blades' winner in a 2-1 away win during March 2009?

699.   Which Blades manager signed Chris?

700.   Against which London club did Chris score The Blades' equaliser in the 78th minute during February 2008?

EPHRAIM 'JOCK' DODDS

701. Jock was born in Grangemouth, Scotland, on 7 September in which year – 1915, 1917 or 1919?

702. From which club did Jock join Sheffield United in 1934?

703. How many League appearances did Jock make for The Blades – 158, 168 or 178?

704. Which club signed Jock from Sheffield United for £10,000 in March 1939?

705. In what position did Jock play?

706. How many appearances did Jock make at international level for Scotland, scoring nine goals?

707. Against which club did Jock make his Blades debut on 15 September 1934 in a 0-0 home draw?

708. True or false: Jock played in the 1936 FA Cup final and hit the crossbar in a 1-0 defeat to Arsenal?

709. How many goals did Jock score in the 6-1 victory over Southampton on 16 February 1935?

710. At which club did Jock finish his playing career in 1950?

DEREK PACE

711. True or false: Derek was a striker during his playing days?

712. What was Derek's nickname while at Sheffield United?

713. From which Midlands club did Derek sign in 1957 when he joined The Blades?

714. Which Blades manager signed Derek for Sheffield United?

715. Against which club did Derek make his debut, scoring after only 8 minutes as a Blade in a 4-2 home win?

716. How many League appearances did Derek make for Sheffield United in his football career – 233, 243 or 253?

717. Against which London club did Derek score four goals in a 5-0 home League win during December 1958?

718. How many League goals did Derek score in his Blades career – 120, 140 or 160?

719. In what year did Derek leave Bramall Lane?

720. Following on from the previous question, for which club did he sign when he left The Blades?

CROSSING THE DIVIDE

Match up the player with the year he transferred between Sheffield United and Sheffield Wednesday

721. Bernard Shaw   1990 (joined Sheffield United)

722. Alan Quinn   1972 (joined Sheffield United)

723. Joe Cockroft   2004 (joined Sheffield United)

724. Wilf Rostron   2005 (joined Sheffield United)

725. Alan Warboys   1948 (joined Sheffield United)

726. Imre Varadi   1989 (joined Sheffield United)

727. Terry Curran   1973 (joined Sheffield Wednesday)

728. David Ford   1982 (joined Sheffield United)

729. Brian Marwood   1971 (joined Sheffield United)

730. Tommy Johnson   1983 (joined Sheffield Wednesday)

GARY NAYSMITH

731. For which country has Gary won full international caps?

732. In what year did Gary sign for The Blades?

733. Following on from the previous question, against which team did Gary make his Sheffield United debut in a 2-2 home draw?

734. From which Premier League club did The Blades sign Gary?

735. How much did Sheffield United pay for Gary?

736. Can you name the manager that signed Gary for The Blades?

737. For which Scottish club did Gary play between 1996 and 2000?

738. What squad number did Gary wear for The Blades during the 2009/10 season?

739. What is Gary's middle name – Andrew, Adrian or Aaron?

740. Where does Gary play – in the middle, on the right or on the left?

STEEL CITY DERBIES

741.   Who is the only player to have scored for both
       Sheffield United (2005) and Sheffield Wednesday
       (2003) in the Steel City derby?

742.   The first competitive Steel City derby took place on 16
       October in which year – 1890, 1893 or 1896?

743.   What is Sheffield United's biggest ever victory over
       Sheffield Wednesday, in a match at Bramall Lane on 8
       September 1951 in front of 51,075?

744.   In January 1952 Sheffield United recorded a 3-1 win
       against Sheffield Wednesday at Hillsborough, but what
       was the gate attendance?

745.   What was the result when Sheffield United met
       Sheffield Wednesday in the Championship on 18
       September 2009 at Bramall Lane in front of 29,210?

746.   The Blades were beaten in the very first meeting in a
       Steel City derby, a friendly on 15 December 1890 at
       Wednesday's Olive Grove ground, but what was the
       score – 1-0, 2-0 or 2-1?

747.   True or false: Sheffield United did the double over
       Sheffield Wednesday in the Division One 1933/34
       season?

748.   On 21 November 1989 in which competition did
       Sheffield Wednesday beat Sheffield United 3-2 after
       extra time?

749.   From 1976 to 1979 which Sheffield United player
       made 67 appearances but never played in a Steel City
       derby?

750.   In the century from October 1893 to October 1993
       how many goalless draws have there been in the Steel
       City derbies?

JAMES BEATTIE

751. **What is James's middle name – Steven, Scott or Simon?**

752. **In what year did James sign for The Blades?**

753. **Which club did James leave to join Sheffield United?**

754. **True or false: James scored on his Blades debut, in a 2-2 home draw?**

755. **Against which team did James score a Blades hat-trick after only 19 minutes, in a 3-0 home win during April 2008?**

756. **How many League goals did James score for Sheffield United in his first season at Bramall Lane – 18, 20 or 22?**

757. **Against which team did James score a brace in a 2-1 away win during November 2008?**

758. **Which Sheffield United manager signed James for The Blades?**

759. **True or false: James has won a total of five full England caps during his football career?**

760. **For which team did James sign when he left Bramall Lane in 2009?**

POT LUCK - 2

761. Who was the first Blade to captain England?

762. In what year did Owen Morrison move from Sheffield Wednesday to Sheffield United?

763. Who was the first ever player to play for both Sheffield United (1892/93) and Sheffield Wednesday (1893/94), making two appearances for The Blades and one for The Owls?

764. In 1978 Blades manager Harry Haslam signed which Argentinean for £160,000?

765. Who took over as manager of Sheffield United from Neil Warnock in May 2007?

766. Which former Blade won the FA Cup with Wimbledon in 1988?

767. In which season did Sheffield United start with a 10-match unbeaten run, until a George Best goal helped Manchester United to victory at Old Trafford?

768. In which season was a Blades v. Arsenal match the first ever football match to be broadcast on the radio – 1926/27, 1936/37 or 1946/47?

769. In 2004 which player moved to Bramall Lane on a free transfer from rivals Sheffield Wednesday?

770. Who played for The Blades during World War Two and moved to Hillsborough in 1948?

MICHAEL TONGE

771. Against which team did Michael score a brace in a 3-1 away League win during October 2002?

772. What was the match result when Michael scored against Fulham in a Premier League home win during January 2007?

773. Against which Premier League team did Michael score a brace in a 2-1 home win in the League Cup semi-final, 1st leg, during January 2003?

774. How many League goals did Michael score for The Blades during the 2001/02 season?

775. In which year was Michael born in Manchester – 1981, 1982 or 1983?

776. Against which team did Michael make his Sheffield United League debut during April 2001 in a 1-0 home defeat?

777. What is Michael's middle name – William, Wayne or Willis?

778. In what position does Michael play?

779. True or false: Blades manager Steve Bruce signed Michael when he was released by Manchester City?

780. For which team did Michael sign when he left Bramall Lane in 2008?

JOHN HARRIS

781. John was born in Glasgow on 30 June in which year – 1913, 1915 or 1917?

782. What job did John have with Sheffield Wednesday in 1977?

783. John was captain of which team when they won the First Division championship in 1955?

784. From which club did John join Sheffield United as manager in 1959?

785. Which former Blades acting manager did John succeed on 20 April 1959?

786. For which club did John play between 1934 and 1939?

787. John was manager of The Blades from 1959 to 1973, but what was his job title in season 1968/69?

788. In what position did John play?

789. At which club did John start his professional playing career in 1932?

790. Between 1939 and 1943 John made 121 guest appearances, scoring 15 goals, for which south coast club?

JAMIE WARD

791. In what year did Jamie join Sheffield United?

792. Following on from the previous question, against which team did Jamie make his Blades debut, in a 1-0 home League defeat?

793. Against which team did Jamie score The Blades' first goal after 7 minutes, in a 3-2 home win during September 2009?

794. Which Blades squad number did Jamie wear during the 2009/10 season?

795. Against which team did Jamie score his first Sheffield United goal, on only his second appearance for club?

796. At which Midlands club did Jamie start his career as a trainee?

797. In which year was Jamie born – 1984, 1985 or 1986?

798. From which club did Jamie sign when he joined The Blades?

799. For which country has Jamie won seven under-21 international caps?

800. What is Jamie's middle name – John, Jacob or Jake?

ANSWERS

CLUB HISTORY & RECORDS

1.   *1889 (22 March)*
2.   *The Blades*
3.   *32,609*
4.   *1899*
5.   *631*
6.   *Cardiff City*
7.   *Leeds United*
8.   *Harry Johnson*
9.   *Sheffield Wednesday*
10.   *S2 4SU*

TONY CURRIE

11.   *1950*
12.   *54*
13.   *Watford*
14.   *True*
15.   *TC*
16.   *Football in the Community co-ordinator*
17.   *12*
18.   *William*
19.   *17*
20.   *Leeds United*

CLUB HONOURS

21.	*Division One Champions*	*1897/98*
22.	*Championship Runners-up*	*2005/06*
23.	*Division Two Runners-up*	*1970/71*
24.	*Division Four Champions*	*1981/82*
25.	*FA Cup Winners (first time)*	*1898/99*
26.	*Division One Runners-up*	*1899/1900*
27.	*Division Two Champions*	*1952/53*
28.	*FA Cup Runners-up*	*1935/36*

29.	Division Three Runners-up	1988/89
30.	Championship Play-off Runners-up	2008/09

BRIAN DEANE

31.	Christopher
32.	True
33.	3
34.	3
35.	West Ham United
36.	14
37.	Burnley
38.	Doncaster Rovers
39.	Benfica
40.	Ipswich Town

WHERE DID THEY GO? – 1

41.	Alan Birchenall	Chelsea
42.	Jon Harley	Burnley
43.	Michael Tonge	Stoke City
44.	Alf Ringstead	Mansfield Town
45.	Paul Peschisolido	Derby County
46.	Roy Warhurst	Birmingham City
47.	Fred Smith	Manchester City
48.	Alan Warboys	Bristol Rovers
49.	Derek Pace	Notts County
50.	Ephraim 'Jock' Dodds	Blackpool

PADDY KENNY

51.	Goalkeeper
52.	Bury
53.	Republic of Ireland
54.	1978
55.	Neil Warnock

56. **Bradford Park Avenue**

57. **Coventry City**

58. **2002**

59. **Joseph**

60. **2003**

MANAGERS – 1

61.	**Neil Warnock**	**1999-2007**
62.	**John Harris (second spell)**	**1969-73**
63.	**Teddy Davison**	**1932-52**
64.	**Steve Bruce**	**1998-99**
65.	**Ken Furphy**	**1973-75**
66.	**Howard Kendall**	**1995-97**
67.	**Ian Porterfield**	**1981-86**
68.	**Joe Mercer**	**1955-58**
69.	**Arthur Rowley**	**1968-69**
70.	**Billy McEwan**	**1986-88**

2009/2010

71. **Phil Roebuck**

72. **Middlesbrough**

73. **Chris Morgan**

74. **Matthew Kilgallon**

75. **Kevin Blackwell**

76. **Kevin McCabe**

77. **Reading**

78. **Stephen Quinn, Jamie Ward and David Cotterill**

79. **Kyel Reid**

80. **Glen Little**

NATIONALITIES – 1

81.	**Bruno Ribeiro**	**Portuguese**
82.	**Roger Nilsen**	**Norwegian**

83.	Gary Naysmith	Scottish
84.	Vass Borbokis	Greek
85.	Ernest Needham	English
86.	Petr Katchouro	Belarusian
87.	Ahmed Fathi	Egyptian
88.	Dean Saunders	Welsh
89.	Peter Boyle	Irish
90.	David Carney	Australian

2008/2009

91.	Billy Sharp
92.	Burnley
93.	Preston North End
94.	Cardiff City
95.	James Beattie
96.	3rd
97.	22
98.	Kevin Blackwell
99.	Jamie Ward
100.	True

WHERE DID THEY COME FROM? – 1

101.	Wayne Allison	Tranmere Rovers
102.	Brian Deane (first spell)	Doncaster Rovers
103.	Gordon Cowans	Wolverhampton Wanderers
104.	Vinnie Jones	Leeds United
105.	Lee Hendrie	Aston Villa
106.	Neil Shipperley	Crystal Palace
107.	Marcus Bent	Port Vale
108.	Colin Addison	Arsenal
109.	Barry Hayles	Fulham
110.	Gary Speed	Bolton Wanderers

DIVISION TWO RUNNERS-UP – 1970/1971

111.	Eddie Colquhoun
112.	John Harris
113.	Leicester City
114.	21
115.	Alan Woodward
116.	Portsmouth
117.	Trevor Hockley
118.	True: 3 wins and 4 draws
119.	Bill Dearden
120.	82nd

POSITIONS IN THE LEAGUE – 1

121.	2008/09, 80 points	3rd
122.	1976/77, 40 points	11th
123.	1993/94, 42 points	20th
124.	1893/94, 31 points	10th
125.	1936/37, 46 points	7th
126.	1984/85, 44 points	18th
127.	2003/04, 71 points	8th
128.	1963/64, 43 points	12th
129.	1925/26, 46 points	5th
130.	1957/58, 52 points	6th

DIVISION TWO RUNNERS-UP – 1989/1990

131.	Leeds United
132.	24
133.	Dave Bassett
134.	Simon Tracey
135.	21
136.	Brighton & Hove Albion
137.	Tony Agana
138.	True: 3 wins and 4 draws

139.   2-0 to Sheffield United

140.   Bradford City

POSITIONS IN THE LEAGUE – 2

141.	1969/70, 49 points	6th
142.	2006/07, 38 points	18th
143.	2000/01, 68 points	10th
144.	1981/82, 96 points	1st
145.	1951/52, 41 points	11th
146.	1907/08, 35 points	17th
147.	1949/50, 52 points	3rd
148.	1960/61, 58 points	2nd
149.	1991/92, 57 points	9th
150.	1975/76, 22 points	22nd

KEITH EDWARDS

151.   Striker

152.   Hull City

153.   1957

154.   261: 247 (14)

155.   Leicester City

156.   Notts County

157.   18

158.   Huddersfield Town

159.   Leeds United

160.   143

SQUAD NUMBERS 2009/2010 – 1

161.	Jamie Ward	18
162.	Keith Treacy	26
163.	Ryan France	2
164.	James Harper	15
165.	Chris Morgan	5

166.	*Ian Bennett*	*13*
167.	*Andy Taylor*	*16*
168.	*Kyel Reid*	*10*
169.	*Kyle Walker*	*34*
170.	*Darius Henderson*	*7*

2007/2008

171.	*Bryan Robson*
172.	*9th*
173.	*17*
174.	*Colchester United*
175.	*Charlton Athletic*
176.	*James Beattie*
177.	*Ian Bennett*
178.	*Matthew Kilgallon*
179.	*Kevin Beattie*
180.	*19*

WHERE DID THEY GO? – 2

181.	*George Thompson*	*Derby County*
182.	*Harry Johnson*	*Mansfield Town*
183.	*Jimmy Dunne*	*Arsenal*
184.	*Ade Akinbiyi*	*Burnley*
185.	*David Holdsworth*	*Birmingham City*
186.	*Peter Withe*	*Huddersfield Town*
187.	*Danny Webber*	*Portsmouth*
188.	*Len Badger*	*Chesterfield*
189.	*Alan Woodward*	*Tulsa Roughnecks*
190.	*Keith Gillespie*	*Bradford City*

PAUL STANCLIFFE

| 191. | *Central defender* |
| 192. | *Ian* |

89

193. *1958*

194. *278*

195. *Stan*

196. *Rotherham United*

197. *Ian Porterfield*

198. *False: he didn't win any international caps*

199. *Wolverhampton Wanderers*

200. *12*

MANAGERS – 2

201.	*Reg Freeman*	*1952-55*
202.	*Bryan Robson*	*2007-08*
203.	*Harry Haslam*	*1978-80*
204.	*Jimmy Sirrell*	*1975-77*
205.	*Nigel Spackman*	*1997-98*
206.	*John Harris (first spell)*	*1959-68*
207.	*Martin Peters*	*1980-81*
208.	*Dave Bassett*	*1988-95*
209.	*Adrian Heath*	*1999*
210.	*John Nicholson (secretary)*	*1889-1932*

DIVISON THREE RUNNERS-UP – 1988/1989

211. *Dave Bassett*

212. *Wolverhampton Wanderers*

213. *True*

214. *Tony Agana*

215. *25*

216. *Tony Agana (24) and Brian Deane (22)*

217. *Chester City*

218. *Notts County*

219. *True: Sheffield United beat Wolves 2-0 at home and drew 2-2 away*

220. *Reg Brealey*

WHERE DID THEY COME FROM? – 2

221.	Trevor Hockey	Birmingham City
222.	Nigel Spackman	Chelsea
223.	Keith Edwards	Hull City
224.	Adrian Heath	Burnley
225.	Franz Carr	Newcastle United
226.	Billy Sharp	Scunthorpe United
227.	John Barnwell	Nottingham Forest
228.	Bob Hatton	Luton Town
229.	Adrian Littlejohn	Bury
230.	Rob Hulse	Leeds United

DANE WHITEHOUSE

231.	1970
232.	38
233.	Stockport County
234.	Brian Deane
235.	5
236.	Chelsea
237.	Grimsby Town
238.	1988
239.	Dave Bassett
240.	231: 204 (27)

FA CUP WINS

241.	1992/93, 5th round	Sheffield United 2-1 Manchester United
242.	1988/89, 4th round replay	Colchester United 0-2 Sheffield United
243.	1962/63, 4th round	Port Vale 1-2 Sheffield United
244.	1951/52, 5th round	Southend United 1-2 Sheffield United

245.	1898/99, quarter-final	Nottingham Forest 0-1 Sheffield United
246.	1935/36, quarter-final	Sheffield United 3-1 Tottenham Hotspur
247.	1974/75, 3rd round	Sheffield United 2-0 Bristol City
248.	1997/98, 5th round	Sheffield United 1-0 Reading
249.	2004/05, 3rd round	Sheffield United 3-1 Aston Villa
250.	1995/96, 3rd round replay	Sheffield United 1-0 Arsenal

LEN BADGER

251.	458: 457 (1)
252.	1962
253.	Leyton Orient
254.	John Harris
255.	1945
256.	13
257.	Fulham
258.	Right back
259.	7
260.	Chesterfield

SQUAD NUMBERS 2009/2010 – 2

261.	Stephen Quinn	28
262.	Ched Evans	9
263.	Gary Naysmith	3
264.	Mark Bunn	23
265.	Lee Williamson	12
266.	Matthew Kilgallon	6
267.	Jordan Stewart	19
268.	David Cottrill	11

269.	Nick Montgomery	4
270.	Glen Little	25

2006/2007

271.	Liverpool
272.	Rob Hulse
273.	Middlesbrough
274.	Danny Webber
275.	Jon Stead
276.	8
277.	Neil Warnock
278.	18th
279.	West Ham United
280.	Christian Nadé

CAPS FOR MY COUNTRY

281.	Barry Hayles	10 caps for Jamaica (0 goals)
282.	Trevor Hockey	9 caps for Wales (1 goal)
283.	Alf Ringstead	20 caps for Republic of Ireland (7 goals)
284.	Peter Ndlovu	100 caps for Zimbabwe (38 goals)
285.	Peter Withe	11 caps for England (1 goal)
286.	Gary Speed	85 caps for Wales (7 goals)
287.	Paul Peschisolido	53 caps for Canada (11 goals)
288.	Keith Gillespie	86 caps for Northern Ireland (2 goals)
289.	Patrick Suffo	29 caps for Cameroon (4 goals)
290.	Jostein Flo	53 caps for Norway (11 goals)

2005/2006

291. **Ade Akinbiyi**

292. **2nd**

293. **Reading**

294. **Phil Jagielka**

295. **Michael Tonge and Ade Akinbiyi**

296. **David Unsworth**

297. **Leicester City**

298. **Paddy Kenny and Phil Jagielka**

299. **Neil Shipperley**

300. **26**

NATIONALITIES – 2

301.	**Li Tie**	**Chinese**
302.	**Bill Foulke**	**English**
303.	**Colin Hill**	**Irish**
304.	**Paul Peschisolido**	**Canadian**
305.	**Shaun Murphy**	**Australian**
306.	**Alex Forbes**	**Scottish**
307.	**Paul Ifill**	**Barbadian**
308.	**Olivier Tébily**	**Ivorian**
309.	**Nathan Blake**	**Welsh**
310.	**Paddy Kenny**	**Northern Irish**

LEGENDS

311. **Glyn Hodges**

312. **Colin Morris**

313. **Bill Russell**

314. **Jimmy Hagan**

315. **Bob Cain**

316. **Simon Tracey**

317. **Alan Hodgkinson**

318. **Bill Dearden**

| 319. | Gil Reece |
| 320. | Albert Cox |

PLAYING YEARS AT THE CLUB – 1

321.	Harry Johnson	1916-31
322.	Geoff Salmons (first spell)	1966-74
323.	Albert Nightingale	1941-48
324.	Tommy Hoyland	1949-61
325.	Michael Brown	2000-04
326.	Alan Kelly	1992-99
327.	Joe Shaw	1945-66
328.	Bobby Barclay (first spell)	1931-37
329.	Simon Tracey	1988-2003
330.	Alf Common	1901-04

ALAN KELLY

331.	Preston North End
332.	34
333.	1968
334.	Blackburn Rovers
335.	Goalkeeper
336.	Dave Bassett
337.	Arsenal
338.	216: 213 (3)
339.	Alan Kelly Sr
340.	False: he never scored a goal for Sheffield United

POSITIONS THEY PLAYED – 1

341.	Graham Shaw	Left back
342.	Tony Agana	Striker
343.	Mick Speight	Midfielder
344.	Tony Kenworthy	Defender
345.	Paddy Kenny	Goalkeeper

346.	Jimmy Hagan	Inside forward
347.	Gerry Summers	Left half
348.	Walter Rickett	Winger
349.	Ronnie Simpson	Outside left
350.	Bill Cook	Right back

2004/2005

351. Neil Warnock

352. 8th

353. Andy Gray

354. Leeds United

355. Steven Kabba and Andy Gray

356. Danny Cullip

357. Leigh Bromby and Phil Jagielka

358. Paul Shaw

359. 18

360. Alan Quinn

TOP LEAGUE APPEARANCES

361.	Len Badger	457 (1)
362.	Cec Coldwell	409 (1)
363.	Ernest Needham	464
364.	Graham Shaw	439
365.	Joe Shaw	632
366.	Billy Gillespie	448
367.	George Green	393
368.	Alan Hodgkinson	576
369.	Fred Tunstall	437
370.	Alan Woodward	536 (2)

DIVISION ONE PLAY-OFF RUNNERS-UP – 1997

371. Crystal Palace

372. 1-0

373. *Ipswich Town*

374. *Howard Kendall*

375. *Charlton Athletic*

376. *Mike McDonald*

377. *Middlesbrough*

378. *Southend United*

379. *5th*

380. *Petr Katchouro*

PLAYING YEARS AT THE CLUB – 2

381.	*Bill Russell*	*1957-63*
382.	*Phil Jagielka*	*1999-2007*
383.	*Ted Burgin*	*1949-57*
384.	*Mick Jones*	*1962-67*
385.	*George Utley*	*1913-21*
386.	*James Beattie*	*2007-09*
387.	*Keith Eddy*	*1972-76*
388.	*Ian Bryson*	*1988-93*
389.	*Jimmy Dunne*	*1926-33*
390.	*John Flynn*	*1969-78*

2003/2004

391. *8th*

392. *West Ham United*

393. *Coventry City*

394. *Paul Peschisolido and Peter Ndlovu*

395. *Andy Gray*

396. *Michael Tonge*

397. *Jack Lester*

398. *Ashley Ward*

399. *Neil Warnock*

400. *20*

POSITIONS THEY PLAYED – 2

401.	Tony Currie	Midfielder
402.	Jack Smith	Goalkeeper
403.	Jimmy Simmons	Forward
404.	James Beattie	Striker
405.	Gil Preece	Outside left
406.	Cec Coldwell	Right back
407.	Len Allchurch	Outside right
408.	Albert Cox	Fullback
409.	Harold Pantling	Wing half
410.	Tommy Morren	Centre half

CHAMPIONSHIP PLAY-OFF RUNNERS-UP – 2003

411. Wolverhampton Wanderers

412. Millennium Stadium, Cardiff

413. Nottingham Forest

414. Michael Brown and Peter Ndlovu

415. Bradford City

416. Neil Warnock

417. 3rd

418. 23

419. 16

420. Burnley

TOP LEAGUE GOALSCORERS

421.	Jimmy Dunne	143
422.	Billy Gillespie	127
423.	Jimmy Hagan	117
424.	Alan Woodward	158
425.	Ephraim 'Jock' Dodds	113
426.	Keith Edwards	143
427.	Harry Johnson	201
428.	Joe Kitchen	105

| 429. | Derek Pace | 140 |
| 430. | Fred Tunstall | 129 |

ALAN WOODWARD

431. Winger

432. 1946

433. Woody

434. Number 7

435. Liverpool

436. Ipswich Town

437. 18

438. Southampton

439. Tulsa Roughnecks

440. 158

HOW MUCH DID THEY PAY? – 1

441.	Paul Beesley from Leyton Orient, 1990	£360,000
442.	Paul Garner from Huddersfield Town, 1975	£59,555
443.	Tony Currie from Watford, 1968	£26,500
444.	Jim Brown from Chesterfield, 1974	£80,000
445.	John Flynn from Workington, 1969	£5,000
446.	Arthur Brown from gainsborough Trinity, 1902	£1,600
447.	Keith Edwards from Hull City, 1981	£100,000
448.	Brian Gayle from Ipswich Town, 1991	£750,000
449.	Jimmy Hagan from Derby County, 1938	£2,925
450.	Simon Tracey from Wimbledon, 1988	£12,500

GARY SPEED

451. 2008

452. 85

453. Andrew

454. Leeds United

455. Everton

456. **Wolverhampton Wanderers**

457. **Charlton Athletic**

458. **Watford**

459. **Bolton Wanderers**

460. **Bristol City**

NEIL WARNOCK

461. **1948**

462. **Sheffield**

463. **Chesterfield**

464. **326**

465. **True**

466. **8**

467. **4**

468. **True**

469. **Scarborough**

470. **Crystal Palace**

CAPTAINS

471. **1945/46**   **Jack Pickering**

472. **1950/51**   **Harry Latham**

473. **1957/58**   **Cec Coldwell**

474. **1964/65**   **Joe Shaw**

475. **1966/67**   **Len Badger**

476. **1972/73**   **Eddie Colquhoun**

477. **1977/78**   **Alan Woodward**

478. **1981/82**   **Stewart Houston**

479. **1984/85**   **Paul Stancliffe**

480. **1992/93**   **Bryan Gayle**

ALF RINGSTEAD

481. **1927**

482. **Northwich Victoria**

483. £2,500

484. 105

485. 20

486. Outside right

487. Mansfield Town

488. 247

489. Teddy Davison

490. Coventry City

KEVIN BLACKWELL

491. Goalkeeper

492. 2008

493. Bryan Robson

494. Leeds United

495. 1958

496. Patrick

497. 0-0

498. True

499. Boston United

500. True

JIMMY HAGAN

501. 1918

502. Peterborough United

503. 16

504. Swansea Town

505. West Ham United

506. 361

507. Sheffield Wednesday

508. Inside forward

509. Denmark

510. West Bromwich Albion

DAVE BASSETT

511.	1944
512.	True
513.	Watford
514.	Billy McEwan
515.	Nottingham Forest
516.	2nd
517.	Reg Brealey
518.	Dennis Wise
519.	True: 1988/89 (finished 2nd in Division Three) and 1989/90 (finished 2nd in Division Two)
520.	1995

JOE SHAW

521.	County Durham
522.	714
523.	Liverpool
524.	Chesterfield
525.	8
526.	West Ham United
527.	Upton Colliery
528.	York City
529.	Centre half
530.	632

CHAIRMAN

531.	1943/44 Albert J. Platt
532.	1954/55 Frank Copestake
533.	1955/56 E. Senior Atkin
534.	1958/59 E. Blacow Yates
535.	1969/70 Dick Wragg
536.	1975/76 John Hassall
537.	1981/82 Reg Brealey

538. 1991/92 Paul Woolhouse

539. 1996/97 Mike McDonald

540. 1998/99 Kevin McCabe

MATCH THE YEAR – 1

541. Alan Hodgkinson played his last League
    game for The Blades   1971

542. Sheffield United were FA Cup runners-up
    to Arsenal   1936

543. Umbro first sponsored the Sheffield United kit   1973

544. Michael Tonge was born   1983

545. Kevin Blackwell became manager of
    Sheffield United   2008

546. Bramall Lane hosted the world's first ever
    floodlit football match   1878

547. Cec Coldwell took charge for his second spell
    as acting manager   1977

548. Sheffield United reached the semi-final
    of the League Cup   2003

549. Ian Bryson was born   1962

550. Len Badger was born   1945

COLIN MORRIS

551. Midfielder

552. 1953

553. Burnley

554. Blackpool

555. 4

556. Ian Porterfield

557. 240: 235 (5)

558. Lee Morris

559. 84

560. Scarborough

HOW MUCH DID THEY PAY? – 2

561.	Billy Gillespie from Leeds City, 1912	£500
562.	James Beattie from Everton, 2007	£4,000,000
563.	Paul Ifill from Millwall, 2005	£800,000
564.	Steve Kabba from Crystal Palace, 2002	£250,000
565.	Ched Evans from Manchester City, 2009	£3,000,000
566.	Michael Brown from Manchester City, 2000	£400,000
567.	Carl Asaba from Gillingham, 2001	£92,500
568.	Andy Woodward from Bury, 2000	£33,000
569.	Simon Francis from Bradford City, 2004	£200,000
570.	Jamie Ward from Chesterfield, 2009	£330,000

SIMON TRACEY

571.	1967
572.	Peter
573.	Goalkeeper
574.	1988
575.	Wimbledon
576.	False: he never won any international caps
577.	Dave Bassett
578.	10
579.	West Bromwich Albion
580.	2003

MATCH THE YEAR – 2

581.	Chris Morgan joined Sheffield United from Barnsley	2003
582.	George Utley led The Blades out for the FA Cup final	1915
583.	Sheffield United received £4 million for Phil Jagielka from Everton	2007
584.	Matthew Kilgallon was born	1984
585.	Sheffield United beat Burnley	1929

586.	Port Vale lost 10-0 to Sheffield United at Vale Park	1892
587.	Darius Henderson signed from Watford for £2 million	2008
588.	Laurent D'Jaffo signed from Stockport County for £175,000	2000
589.	Ryan France was born	1980
590.	Colin Collindridge was the Division One season's top goalscorer	1947

TONY AGANA

591.	Striker
592.	Watford
593.	Barnsley
594.	True
595.	118: 105 (13)
596.	Dave Bassett
597.	24
598.	West Bromwich Albion
599.	42
600.	Notts County

BLADES WINS AGAINST THE OWLS

601.	Division One, 3 March 1934	Blades 5-1 Owls
602.	Division One, 4 October 1919	Blades 3-0 Owls
603.	Championship, 18 February 2006	Owls 1-2 Blades
604.	Division Two, 3 October 1970	Blades 3-2 Owls
605.	Division One, 4 February 1967	Blades 1-0 Owls
606.	FA Cup, 22 February 1928	Blades 4-1 Owls
607.	Division Two, 21 January 1950	Blades 2-0 Owls
608.	Division One, 8 April 1905	Blades 4-2 Owls
609.	Division Two, 5 January 1952	Owls 1-3 Blades
610.	Division One, 5 September 1964	Owls 0-2 Blades

PHIL JAGIELKA

611. 1982

612. Everton

613. True

614. Nikodem

615. Swindon Town

616. 18

617. Burnley

618. Leeds United

619. True

620. Neil Warnock

MATCH THE YEAR - 3

621. Jimmy Johnston joined The Blades from
     San Jose Earthquakes   1975

622. Bruce Dyer joined The Blades from Stoke City   2006

623. Derek Hawksworth made his 255th and last
     League appearance for Sheffield United   1958

624. Cliff Mason left The Blades to join Yorkshire
     rivals Leeds United   1962

625. Harold Pantling became Sheffield United's
     first player to be sent off twice in a season   1918

626. Lee Morris was sold to Derby County for
     £3 million   1999

627. The Blades launched a fellowship for former
     players   2008

628. Sheffield United were relegated from the
     Premiership for the first time   1994

629. Robert Page joined The Blades from Watford
     for £350,000   2001

630. Roy Warhurst was born   1926

MICHAEL BROWN

631. 1977

632. Tottenham Hotspur

633. Midfielder

634. Robert

635. Manchester City

636. True: December 1999 and January 2000

637. Manchester City

638. Neil Warnock

639. 16

640. Coventry City

POT LUCK – 1

641. Richard Cresswell

642. Jan Aage Fjortoft

643. 88

644. 1967

645. New John Street Stand

646. Derby County

647. Bradford City

648. Left wing

649. Newport County

650. 1975

TREVOR HOCKEY

651. 1943

652. Midfielder

653. Wales

654. Birmingham City

655. John Harris

656. 68

657. Norwich City

658. Oxford United

659. **Bradford City**

660. **4**

BLADES GOALKEEPERS

661. **216**

662. **Bill Foulke**

663. **Stefan Postma**

664. **Jack Smith**

665. **Joe Lievesley**

666. **5**

667. **Castleford Town**

668. **314**

669. **Detroit Express**

670. **Ian Bennett**

MICK JONES

671. **3**

672. **David**

673. **Leeds United**

674. **Centre forward**

675. **False: he never managed the club**

676. **1945**

677. **21**

678. **Manchester United**

679. **Manchester City**

680. **63**

WHO AM I?

681. **Bill Foulke**

682. **Jonathon Fortune**

683. **Gordon Cowans**

684. **Ryan Cresswell**

685. **Ryan France**

686.   **Rob Hulse**

687.   **Billy Gillespie**

688.   **Luton Shelton**

689.   **Colin Morris**

690.   **Chris Armstrong**

CHRIS MORGAN

691.   **Paul**

692.   **Central defender**

693.   **Barnsley**

694.   **2003**

695.   **5**

696.   **0-0 (on the opening day of the 2003/04 season)**

697.   **Ipswich Town**

698.   **Coventry City**

699.   **Neil Warnock**

700.   **Queens Park Rangers**

EPHRAIM 'JOCK' DODDS

701.   **1915**

702.   **Lincoln City**

703.   **178**

704.   **Blackpool**

705.   **Centre forward**

706.   **8**

707.   **Burnley**

708.   **True**

709.   **4**

710.   **Lincoln City**

DEREK PACE

711.   **True**

712.   **Doc**

713.   *Aston Villa*

714.   *Joe Mercer*

715.   *Blackburn Rovers*

716.   *253*

717.   *Charlton Athletic*

718.   *140*

719.   *1964*

720.   *Notts County*

CROSSING THE DIVIDE

721.	*Bernard Shaw*	*1973 (joined Sheffield Wednesday)*
722.	*Alan Quinn*	*2004 (joined Sheffield United)*
723.	*Joe Cockroft*	*1948 (joined Sheffield United)*
724.	*Wilf Rostron*	*1989 (joined Sheffield United)*
725.	*Alan Warboys*	*1972 (joined Sheffield United)*
726.	*Imre Varadi*	*1983 (joined Sheffield Wednesday)*
727.	*Terry Curran*	*1982 (joined Sheffield United)*
728.	*David Ford*	*1971 (joined Sheffield United)*
729.	*Brian Marwood*	*1990 (joined Sheffield United)*
730.	*Tommy Johnson*	*2005 (joined Sheffield United)*

GARY NAYSMITH

731.   *Scotland*

732.   *2007*

733.   *Colchester United*

734.   *Everton*

735.   *£1 million*

736.   *Bryan Robson*

737.   *Hearts*

738.   *3*

739.   *Andrew*

740.   *On the left*

STEEL CITY DERBIES

741.   Alan Quinn
742.   1893 (1-1)
743.   Sheffield United 7-3 Sheffield Wednesday
744.   65,000
745.   Sheffield United 3- 2 Sheffield Wednesday
746.   Sheffield Wednesday 2-1 Sheffield United
747.   True: 5-1 at home and 0-1 away
748.   Zenith Data Cup (Full Members Cup)
749.   Simon Stainrod
750.   2 (Division Two, 29 October 1938 and 12 April 1971)

JAMES BEATTIE

751.   Scott
752.   2007
753.   Everton
754.   True: against Colchester on the opening day of the 2007/08 season
755.   Leicester City
756.   22
757.   Barnsley
758.   Bryan Robson
759.   True
760.   Stoke City

POT LUCK - 2

761.   Ernest Needham (1901)
762.   2003
763.   Billy Mellars
764.   Alex Sabella
765.   Bryan Robson
766.   Vinnie Jones
767.   1971/72

768.   1926/27

769.   Leigh Bromby

770.   Walter Rickett

MICHAEL TONGE

771.   Wolverhampton Wanderers

772.   2-0 to Sheffield United

773.   Liverpool

774.   3

775.   1983

776.   Wimbledon

777.   William

778.   Midfielder

779.   False: he was released by Manchester United

780.   Stoke City

JOHN HARRIS

781.   1917

782.   Chief scout

783.   Chelsea

784.   Chester City

785.   Archie Clark

786.   Swansea Town

787.   General manager

788.   Defender

789.   Swindon Town

790.   Southampton

JAMIE WARD

791.   2009

792.   Doncaster Rovers

793.   Sheffield Wednesday

794.   18

NOTES

NOTES

OTHER BOOKS BY CHRIS COWLIN:

* Celebrities' Favourite Football Teams

* The British TV Sitcom Quiz Book

* The Cricket Quiz Book

* The Gooners Quiz Book

* The Horror Film Quiz Book

* The Official Aston Villa Quiz Book

* The Official Birmingham City Quiz Book

* The Official Brentford Quiz Book

* The Official Bristol Rovers Quiz Book

* The Official Burnley Quiz Book

* The Official Bury Quiz Book

* The Official Carlisle United Quiz Book

* The Official Carry On Quiz Book

* The Official Chesterfield Football Club Quiz Book

* The Official Colchester United Quiz Book

* The Official Coventry City Quiz Book

* The Official Doncaster Rovers Quiz Book

* The Official Greenock Morton Quiz Book

* The Official Heart of Midlothian Quiz Book

* The Official Hereford United Quiz Book

* The Official Hull City Quiz Book

OTHER BOOKS BY CHRIS COWLIN:

* The Official Leicester City Quiz Book

* The Official Macclesfield Town Quiz Book

* The Official Norwich City Football Club Quiz

* The Official Notts County Quiz Book

* The Official Peterborough United Quiz Book

* The Official Port Vale Quiz Book

* The Official Rochdale AFC Quiz Book

* The Official Rotherham United Quiz Book

* The Official Sheffield United Quiz Book

* The Official Shrewsbury Town Quiz Book

* The Official Stockport County Quiz Book

* The Official Watford Football Club Quiz Book

* The Official West Bromwich Albion Quiz Book

* The Official Wolves Quiz Book

* The Official Yeovil Town Quiz Book

* The Reality Television Quiz Book

* The Southend United Quiz Book

* The Sunderland AFC Quiz Book

* The Ultimate Derby County Quiz Book

* The West Ham United Quiz Book

www.apexpublishing.co.uk